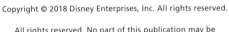

Autumn
Publishing

Published in 2018
by Autumn Publishing
Cottage Farm
Sywell
NN6 0BJ
www.igloobooks.com

GOL002 0718
2 4 6 8 10 9 7 5 3 1
ISBN 978-1-78810-837-9

Printed and manufactured in China

MY MEGA
BOOK OF FUN

CONTENTS

Autumn
Publishing

FROZEN

The kingdom of Arendelle was a happy place, located next to a deep fjord. At night, the Northern Lights often lit up the skies in beautiful patterns. But the king and queen lived with a secret worry.

Their eldest daughter, Elsa, had magical powers. She could freeze things and create snow, even in the summer! Their youngest daughter, Anna, just adored her older sister. The two loved to play together in the snowy playgrounds that Elsa created.

One night, Elsa's magic accidentally hit Anna.

The king and queen rushed the girls to the realm of the trolls for some help. The trolls reassured them that Anna would recover.

They also warned that Elsa's powers would get stronger, so she should learn to control them.

Back in Arendelle, Elsa struggled to stay in control of her powers at all times. She decided to stay away from Anna, to keep her little sister safe.

The trolls had changed Anna's memories, so she didn't remember Elsa's magic. Instead, she grew up thinking that Elsa wanted nothing to do with her.

By the time Elsa was crowned queen, the sisters had grown far apart. They hardly knew each other at all.

Having grown up mostly by herself, Anna had felt lonely for a long time. So she was thrilled to meet handsome Prince Hans on the day of Elsa's coronation.

Anna and Hans liked each other straightaway. At the coronation party, they danced and talked all night long.

Prince Hans asked for Anna's hand in marriage and she quickly agreed. But Elsa reacted angrily. "You can't marry someone you've just met!"

Anna argued back. "I can't live like this any more! I'm always alone!"

Then Elsa got upset and an icy blast shot from her hand – in front of everyone!

Worried that her secret had been exposed and afraid she would hurt someone, Elsa fled from the castle. Everything froze behind her as she ran away.

Once Elsa had climbed up into the mountains, she felt calm. Now that she was all alone, she was able to let out her powers for the first time ever! She created whirls of snow, ice and even an ice palace.

She was able to be herself and it felt wonderful!

Meanwhile, Anna realised that Elsa had been away
for all those years because she needed to hide
her magic. Anna decided to go after Elsa – now that
her secret was out, they could be together!

Anna headed up the mountain, but her horse threw
her into the snow. Luckily, she was able to find shelter
in a nearby shop.

Inside, Anna met a young man covered in frost. He was cross because he was an ice harvester and the midsummer snowstorm was ruining his business.

He also knew where the storm was coming from. That meant he could take her to Elsa!

Anna hired the young man, who was called Kristoff,
to take her up the North Mountain to find Elsa.
His reindeer, Sven, came along for the journey, too.

As they neared the top of the mountain, the trio saw
a beautiful wintery landscape. Elsa had covered everything
with glistening, sparkling ice.

Elsa had also created
a snowman... who was alive!

The snowman's name was Olaf and he
was excited to hear that Anna planned
to bring back summer, because he loved
the idea of warm weather.
He offered to take them to Elsa.

As the group moved on,
they found the fantastic ice
palace that Elsa had created
with her magical powers.

Anna was impressed by Elsa's powers and sparkling ice palace. But she really wanted Elsa to come back home.

Elsa thought the people of Arendelle wouldn't accept her and she was still afraid that she would hurt them.

The two girls argued.
Although Elsa didn't intend to hurt Anna, she hit her sister in the chest with a blast of ice.

Then she created another snowman, named Marshmallow, who was much bigger than Olaf. The huge snowman made sure that Anna, Kristoff, Sven and Olaf left the mountain quickly!

Once they were safe, Kristoff noticed that Anna's hair was turning white. Kristoff took her to the trolls to see if their magic could help.

The trolls explained that Elsa's blast had hit Anna in the heart and that soon she would freeze completely! But they added, "An act of true love will thaw a frozen heart."

Olaf and Kristoff decided to hurry Anna back to Arendelle so Hans could give her a true love's kiss.

Meanwhile, back in Arendelle, Hans was helping everyone during the storm. Then, Anna's horse arrived back in Arendelle without her!

Hans took a group out to find Anna... but they found Elsa
first. Elsa was forced to defend herself against some of the men.
Finally, she was taken back to Arendelle as a prisoner!
The men were convinced she was dangerous.

Kristoff brought Anna to Arendelle, but Hans refused
to kiss her. He didn't love her! He had only wanted to rule
Arendelle, but had to make sure the sisters were out of the
way first.

Anna was devastated. But Olaf realised that Kristoff loved
Anna, so his kiss could still save her. Anna made her way
towards Kristoff. Then, she saw her sister in danger...

Anna threw herself in front of Elsa, just in time to block a blow from Hans's sword.

At that moment, Anna transformed into solid
ice. The sword shattered against her icy body.

Elsa realised that Anna had tried to protect her. She flung her arms around her frozen sister and cried. She didn't want to lose her sister.

Suddenly, Anna began to melt. Anna's act of true love for her sister meant that the spell was broken!

Then, with Anna's love and faith, Elsa managed to bring back summer.

The sisters hugged and promised to love each other from then on. The people of Arendelle saw everything and they welcomed Elsa home.

Kristoff decided to stay in Arendelle and so did Olaf – with the help of a little winter cloud to keep him cool. Best of all, the sisters were back together and happy at last!

ICE-TASTIC ACTIVITIES

Elsa and her younger sister, Anna, are inseparable.
They love playing and having fun together.

Look for the five differences between these two pictures
of young Elsa and Anna building a snowman.

Answers on
page 163

35

Elsa has magical powers. She can create snow and ice!
One night, she makes a winter wonderland in the castle.

The sisters have a snowball fight, slide around on
the ice and build a funny-looking snowman!

Can you help Anna and Elsa count all the snowflakes,
carrots and twigs? Use the sums to help you.

1 + 1 = ...

2 + 2 = ...

4 + 5 = ...

5 + 3 = ...

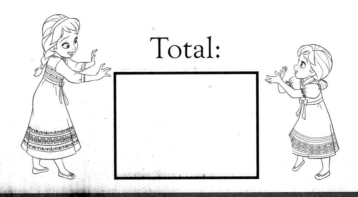

Total:

Answers on page 163

One of Elsa's icy spells accidentally hits Anna. Elsa calls to the king and queen for help as Anna shivers with cold.

Anna and Elsa's worried parents take them to the realm of the trolls.
They hope the trolls' mystical powers will be able to heal Anna.

The trolls make Anna better, but they warn that Elsa's powers could grow and become dangerous. The king gives Elsa gloves to help control her magic.

The king wants to keep his daughters safe,
so he puts up walls around the castle.

Elsa is terrified that she might hurt Anna again.
She stops answering when Anna knocks on her door.

Anna feels alone. She doesn't understand
why her sister won't play with her anymore.

The two sisters grow up, and soon the
time comes for Elsa to become queen.

Can you help Elsa get ready for her coronation?
Draw pretty patterns on her dress to make it special.

Kristoff is an ice harvester, selling ice to people in the hot summer. His best friend is a reindeer named Sven.

Can you tell which two pictures of Sven are
the same? When you find them, colour them in!

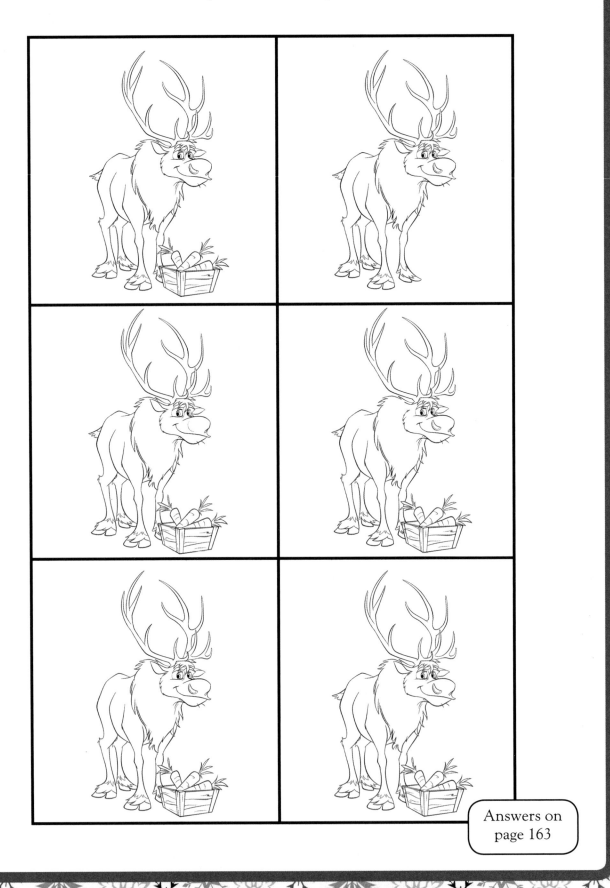

Answers on
page 163

48

Finally, it's coronation day! The castle gates are opened and Anna rushes outside in excitement. She can't wait to meet everyone!

Elsa waits nervously in her room. She is worried that people might notice her icy powers.

Prince Hans has sailed to Arendelle especially for Elsa's coronation day. He comes from the Southern Isles.

Can you find five things in the bottom picture that are different from the top picture? Circle the differences when you find them.

Answers on
page 163

Anna runs along the pier, trips and tumbles into a boat. Prince Hans helps her up. He is honoured to meet a princess of Arendelle.

This picture of Anna and Hans is incomplete. Write the letter of each missing piece in the space where it belongs.

Ⓐ

Ⓑ

Ⓒ

Ⓓ

Answers on page 163

Anna rushes back to the castle just in time for the coronation.

Elsa is ready to be crowned Queen of Arendelle!
Circle the crown that matches the one Elsa is wearing.

A

B

C

D

E

F

Answer on
page 163

Elsa holds the royal sceptre and orb for a moment, then she quickly puts them down before she freezes them.

The people of Arendelle clap and cheer. Elsa looks
very regal in her beautiful dress and crown.

Anna dances with Hans at the coronation ball. They walk and talk together and find out that they have a lot in common.

Anna is sure she has found true love. Hans asks
her to marry him and she says yes!

Anna wants to tell Elsa the good news right away! Which of
the paths will lead Anna and Hans to Queen Elsa?

Start

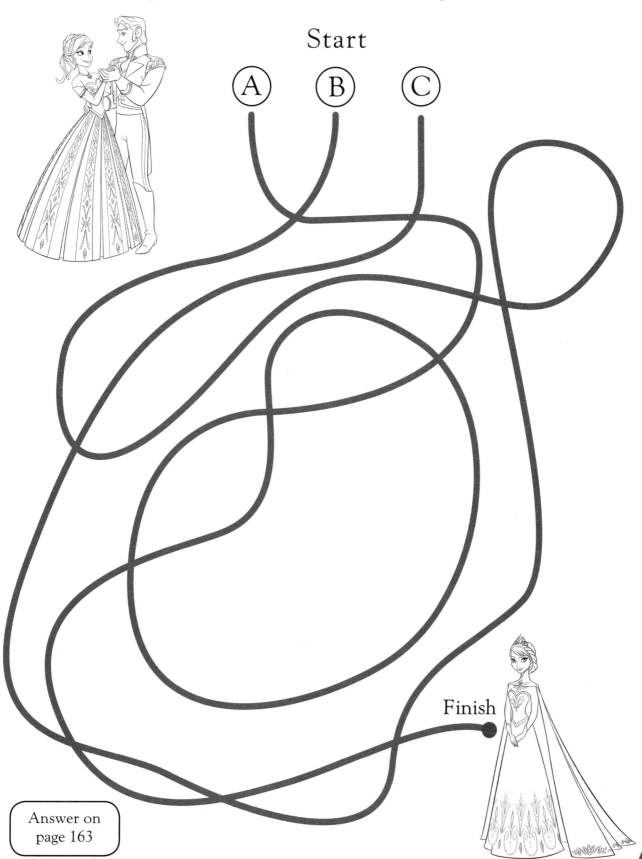

A B C

Finish

Answer on
page 163

Elsa is angry that Anna has got engaged
to someone she just met.

Elsa refuses to bless the marriage. Anna tries to talk
to Elsa, grabs her hand and pulls off her sister's glove.

Elsa storms away in anger. Without her glove, she can't control her magic. Ice bursts from Elsa's hand.

The guests gasp in fright. Anna stands back, shocked by what's happened, and feels worried for her sister.

Elsa's secret magical powers have been revealed, so she runs away across the fjords. Everything in her path freezes and Arendelle is cast into eternal winter.

Anna knows she must go after her sister. She asks
Prince Hans to look after Arendelle while she's away.

Elsa leaves Arendelle far behind her. Now that she doesn't have to hide her powers, she feels free.

Elsa creates a beautiful palace made of sparkling ice on the North Mountain.

Elsa transforms into a snow queen. She conjures up
a shimmering blue dress to wear and changes her hair.

Anna rides through the snowstorm,
searching for her sister.

Anna gets thrown from her horse. She becomes very cold, but soon spots Wandering Oaken's Trading Post and Sauna.

Inside the store, Kristoff is buying supplies. Circle five winter supplies he should buy and five summer supplies he definitely doesn't need!

Answers on page 163

Anna meets Kristoff, who's covered in snow. He tells Anna that
the snowstorm is coming from the North Mountain.

Kristoff argues with Oaken about prices for his supplies and calls Oaken a crook. Oaken gets very angry!

Oaken throws Kristoff out of his store into the snow.

Using the top picture as your guide, number the sections of the
mixed-up picture below to show what order they should go in.

① ② ③ ④ ⑤ ⑥ ⑦ ⑧

○ ○ ○ ○ ○ ○ ○ ○

Answers on
page 163

Anna enters the shed and commands Kristoff to take her to the North Mountain to find Elsa. She brings carrots for Sven to persuade them to help her.

Kristoff agrees and they ride through the forest in Kristoff's sleigh.
Sven gallops as fast as he can! On the way, Anna tells
Kristoff about her fiancé, Hans.

Help Anna, Kristoff and Sven through the mountain maze to reach Elsa's palace. Watch out for wolves, avalanches and cliffs!

Elsa's Palace

Answer on page 164

Anna and Kristoff hear howls nearby. Suddenly, a fearsome pack of wolves appears and starts chasing them!

Sven helps them to escape the wolves by jumping over a deep gorge.
Kristoff slips, but Anna and Sven quickly pull him to safety.

Kristoff is upset that he's lost his sleigh, so Anna promises to replace it. Then, they continue on their journey to the North Mountain.

They meet a new friend in the forest. Join the dots to find out who it is! Then, colour in his buttons, smile and carrot nose.

Start

Anna, Kristoff, Sven and Olaf the snowman
are amazed by how beautiful winter is.

Olaf is a magical snowman. Anna remembers making him with Elsa when they were children. But now he can talk!

Anna asks Olaf if he knows where Elsa is.
Olaf says that he can show Anna the way.

Olaf is made of snow, but he's always dreamed of summer.
He likes to imagine himself sunbathing on a beach!

In each picture below, imagine what Olaf
would sing and then write it in the spaces!

Sven tries to bite Olaf's carrot nose, but Olaf
knows that Sven is just being friendly!

It's time for the friends to continue their journey. They make tracks in the snow. Draw a line from each character to their footprints!

Answers on page 164

Anna is determined to find Elsa. She won't let an icy wall get in her way!

The group gets to a bridge. In order to cross it, they must answer the questions correctly. Colour a step each time you answer a question.

1 Is Elsa Anna's sister?

2 What is Kristoff's reindeer named?

3 What season is Olaf's favourite?

4 Who is Anna engaged to?

5 What is Olaf's nose made from?

6 Who tries to eat Olaf's nose?

Answers on page 164

The friends finally see Elsa's amazing ice palace and they climb up the icy steps to the entrance.

But Elsa isn't happy that Anna has found her.

Anna tries to get Elsa to come home, but Elsa refuses.
She thinks it's too dangerous for her to go back.

Elsa likes being alone and free to use her magical powers.
Anna wants to be friends with Elsa again and she won't give up.

Elsa gets angry and her icy powers accidentally hit Anna in the heart.

Elsa is terrified by the strength of her powers. She's afraid she will hurt Anna again, so she tells her sister to leave.

Elsa makes a giant snowman to scare away Anna and her friends.
Olaf names the giant snowman Marshmallow!

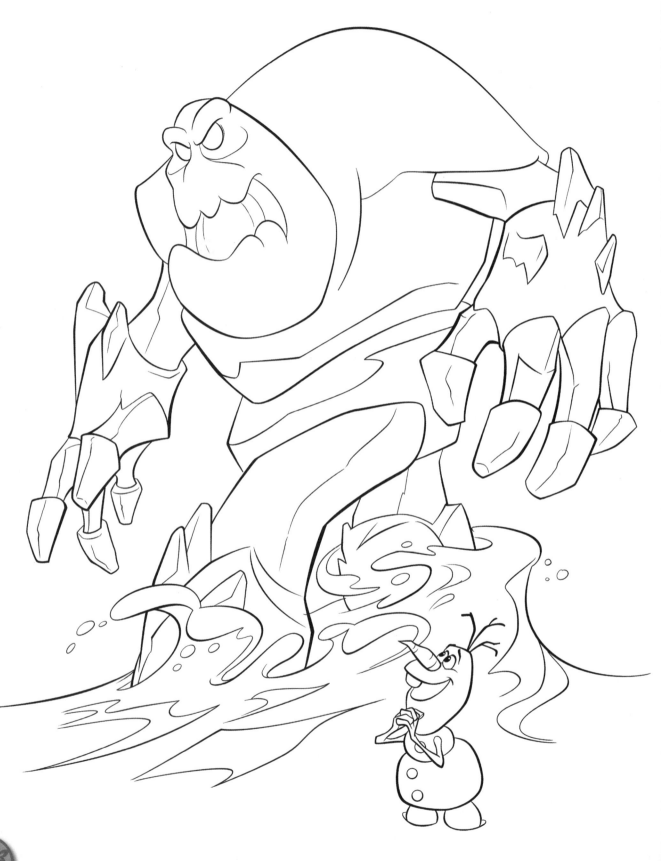

Look for the shadow that matches Elsa's picture exactly.

Answer on page 164

Anna throws a snowball at Marshmallow, which makes him very angry! Can you count all the snowballs in the picture?

Total:

Answer on page 164

Kristoff and Anna run away from Marshmallow as fast
as they can, until they get to the mountain's edge.

They use a rope to escape down the cliff, but then Marsmhallow starts pulling them up again.

Anna cuts the rope and they land safely in the soft, powdery snow.
Kristoff notices Anna's hair turning white. It must be because of Elsa's spell!

Elsa doesn't know how to reverse her spell and end winter.

Meanwhile, Anna's horse arrives back in Arendelle
without her. Prince Hans is worried!

So, Hans climbs onto the horse and sets out to find Anna.

Kristoff knows who might be able
to help Anna – his friends, the trolls!

The trolls are magical. They love Kristoff
and want him to marry Anna!

The trolls realise there is ice in Anna's heart, put there by Elsa's spell. They explain that only an act of true love can melt the ice.

Anna begins to freeze from within and she collapses. Kristoff knows he has to get her back to Hans. Surely a kiss from her true love can save her!

The royal guards and Hans arrive at Elsa's palace.
Marshmallow fights them off.

Some of the guards dodge Marshmallow and reach Elsa.

Frightened, Elsa pins a guard against the palace wall using her icy powers.

Elsa summons more magic to defend herself from the guards and Hans.

A guard shoots an arrow and hits an ice chandelier, causing it to come crashing down. It narrowly misses Elsa, who falls to the ground.

Soon, Elsa is back in Arendelle and locked up in the castle dungeon. Hans asks Elsa to bring back summer, but she doesn't know how.

Kristoff takes Anna to the castle and the servants help her inside.
Kristoff is sad to say goodbye to Anna, but he knows she needs Hans.

Anna explains to Hans that he needs to kiss her in order to save her, but he refuses! Hans reveals that his plan is to take over Arendelle.

Hans pours water over the fire and then leaves Anna to freeze.

Anna has no strength left to escape. She's very cold.

Hans lies to the duke and the people of Arendelle,
telling them that Anna is dead because of Elsa.

Elsa turns the chains to ice and shatters them.
Then, she quickly makes her escape.

Sven knows that something's wrong. He tries to tell
Kristoff to go back to Arendelle to help Anna.

Olaf finds Anna in the castle and builds a fire for her. Out of the window, he sees Kristoff and Sven racing back to Arendelle.

Play this game with a friend. Choose who will be Sven and who will be Olaf and take it in turns to fill an empty space in the grid with a drawing of your chosen character. The winner is the first player to make a line of three in any direction.

Anna realises that Kristoff loves her! Her only hope is a true love's kiss from Kristoff. She follows Olaf out of the castle.

Anna grows colder and colder. There isn't much time left!

In the middle of the storm, Elsa finds Hans. He tells Elsa that her spell has killed Anna. Elsa collapses to the ground in grief.

Anna sees Kristoff running towards her. She turns to him, but then she hears the sound of a sword being drawn.

Anna sees Hans approaching Elsa with the sword in his hand.

He raises his sword and gets ready to strike.

With the last of her strength, Anna rushes to protect her sister. At that moment, Anna freezes into solid ice and Hans's sword shatters against her.

Elsa sees that Anna is frozen. She cries out and throws her arms around her sister. Suddenly, Anna begins to thaw!

An act of true love saved Anna! Sacrificing herself
for Elsa caused Anna's frozen heart to melt.

Anna taught Elsa about love. No longer afraid of her powers, Elsa brings summer back to Arendelle.

Olaf begins to thaw in the heat, so Elsa makes a little snow cloud to keep him from melting.

Anna is upset that Hans betrayed her. She never wants to see him again and Hans is banished from Arendelle.

Draw the missing character in each blank square to complete this puzzle.
Hans, Kristoff, Olaf and Sven should appear once in every row and column.

Answers on
page 164

Elsa, Anna, Kristoff and Olaf are so happy that
the spell is broken and winter is over.

Anna gives Kristoff the sleigh she promised him to replace the one he lost. Kristoff is made official ice gatherer for Arendelle!

Elsa loves creating her own ice palace. Design your own amazing ice palace in the space below.

Anna gives Sven some hay to reward him for his bravery.

Help Sven find his friend Olaf, then guide them both back to Kristoff's sleigh!

START

FINISH

Answer on page 164

145

Sometimes when Olaf jumps around, he falls apart!
Anna and Elsa help him out by putting him back together.

Elsa makes an ice rink for the people of Arendelle to enjoy. Anna and Elsa can now play together again, like they did when they were children.

Sven and Olaf are great friends.

Kristoff can't wait for the next adventure.

Anna and Elsa have fun skating on the ice. Follow the lines starting at each letter to find out which leads to Anna and which leads to Elsa.

Answers on page 164

Elsa and Anna are sisters and also best friends.
Nothing will ever come between them again.

The sisters enjoy Elsa's magical gift together!

MELTING HEARTS

It is a beautiful spring day and Anna has planned a picnic for all her friends. Anna leads the way to the mountains.

Olaf is so excited. He loves picnics! He picks some flowers on the way. Their petals look just like little hearts.

The friends all start searching for heart shapes.
Kristoff bends a twig to make a heart.

At the picnic spot, Kristoff and Anna create an amazing heart-shaped shrub. It's lucky Anna packed the gardening shears!

But then Anna realises she forgot to pack any food, except for some chocolates, which have melted! Everyone bursts out laughing.

Rain starts to pour down and everyone takes cover
under the picnic blanket.

Elsa conjures up an ice shelter. Inside, the sisters use the melted chocolate to make heart-shaped treats for everyone.

The friends munch the chocolate treats and laugh together.
Despite the rain, it is the best picnic ever!

Match these happy Olafs to the correct shadow.

Answers on page 164

Help Kristoff by finding which of the three paths below leads to Sven.

Answer on page 164

Answers

Page 35

Page 38

1 + 1 = 2

2 + 2 = 4

4 + 5 = 9

5 + 3 = 8   Total: 23

Page 48

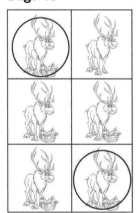

Page 52

Page 54

Page 56

Crown F

Page 61

Path A

Page 73

Page 77

6, 4, 8, 5, 3, 1, 7, 2

Answers

Page 80

Page 91

Kristoff: Sven:

Anna: Olaf:

Page 93

1. Yes
2. Sven
3. Summer
4. Prince Hans
5. Carrot
6. Sven

Page 101

Shadow A is correct

Page 102

20 snowballs

Page 140

Page 145

Page 150

Path C leads to Anna. Path B leads to Elsa.

Page 161

A=2   B=3
C=4   D=1
E =5

Page 162

Path C

FROZEN FEVER

Elsa felt excited and worried in equal measure. Tomorrow was her sister Anna's birthday – and it was the first one in many years that the sisters would spend together!

Elsa rose early, and while Anna was still sleeping, she began the preparations for the big day. She decorated the castle courtyard and used her magical powers to create a beautiful icy topper for the cake.

HAPPY BIRT

Kristoff, Olaf and Sven soon arrived to help. They had made
a birthday banner and they hung it across the courtyard.

Elsa tried not to panic as she watched the wet
paint drip from the banner onto the tables below!
"Are you sure I can leave you in charge here?"
Elsa asked Kristoff.
"Absolutely," he replied.

Elsa headed off to finish the decorations, but then she caught sight of Olaf sneaking a taste of the birthday cake!

"Olaf, what are you doing?" she asked.

"I'm not eating cake," said Olaf.

Elsa leaned close to him. "It's for Anna," she said, with a smile.

Elsa sneaked quietly into Anna's room. "Pssst! Anna," she said.

Anna yawned. "Yeah?" she said, her eyes still closed.

"It's your birthday," said Elsa.

At first, Anna was too sleepy to realise what Elsa was saying, but then...

... she sat straight up!

"It's my birthday!"

While Anna changed into her new birthday dress, Elsa suddenly sneezed and two tiny snowmen appeared. They were snowgies! The creatures fell to the floor and scampered away before the sisters even noticed them.

With a magical wave, Elsa added flowers to her own dress and ice sparkles to Anna's. Although Elsa's head felt a bit funny, nothing was going to stop her from making Anna's birthday really special.

Next, it was time for Anna to find her presents!

"Just follow the string," said Elsa, handing the end of it to her sister.

Anna sprinted down the hall, eager to see where the string would lead her. Anna followed the string down the hallway and under some furniture. She quickened her pace...

... until she ended up at a suit of armour, where she found a beautiful bracelet!

Next, the string led to a cuckoo clock. But instead of a cuckoo, it had a tiny Olaf figure that shouted "SUMMER!" every time the clock opened its doors.

Back in the courtyard, Kristoff and Sven were busy with
the decorations when suddenly a group of the little snowgies
appeared! Kristoff and Sven stared at the tiny snowmen in
disbelief. The snowgies jumped all over the place and made the
punch bowl topple over! Elsa was not going to like this!

"Ah-choo!" Elsa sneezed again as she and Anna zipped down the stairs on Anna's new bicycle.

By now, Anna was worried that Elsa had a cold.

"I'm fine," Elsa said.

Meanwhile, more and more snowgies were arriving in the courtyard and causing chaos! One group knocked down the birthday banner and Olaf had to rehang it.

"All fixed," Olaf announced, putting up the last piece.

But the snowgies seemed determined to destroy the cake. This time, they launched themselves at it!

Kristoff had promised Elsa he would keep the courtyard in order and he didn't want to let her down.

As the sisters reached the doors to the courtyard, Elsa turned to Anna.

"I'm sorry, Anna," she said sadly. "I just wanted to give you one perfect birthday."

"Everything has been absolutely perfect!" Anna said, pushing open the doors.

"Surprise!" called Kristoff.

He had managed to sort everything out just in time! Even he was amazed.

Anna's eyes lit up at the sight of the decorations, her friends and the hundreds of tiny snowgies! "Wow!" she said.

Everyone sang 'Happy Birthday', then Kristoff slid down off
Sven's antlers and knelt before Anna with her birthday cake.
    Anna had a huge smile on her face.
    Sven cut the beautiful cake into slices for everybody to enjoy.
Elsa was proud of all the hard work she had put into the day.
    But she felt another sneeze coming on.
    Elsa really needed to get to bed...

... but not before doing one last thing.

In Arendelle, there was a huge birthday horn, which the king or queen would blow on special birthdays. Anna tried to stop her, but Elsa was determined!

But just as Elsa blew into the horn, she accidentally sneezed...

... and sent a giant snowball flying far across the ocean and right into Hans! The snowball knocked Hans completely off his feet!

After all the fun and games, Elsa let Anna take her up to her bedroom.

It was finally time to rest.

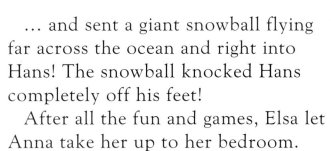

In Elsa's bedroom, Anna gave her big sister some warm soup.
"Best birthday present ever," said Anna.
"Which one?" said Elsa.
"You letting me take care of you," said Anna.
The sisters smiled widely at each other. It really was Anna's best birthday ever, and it was all thanks to Elsa and their wonderful friends.

High on the North Mountain, not long after the birthday party had
ended, Marshmallow opened the doors of the ice palace for Kristoff and
Sven. Olaf came running in, surrounded by the little snowgies! Everyone
had decided the ice palace was the best place for them to live.

Kristoff looked at Marshmallow, shook his head and said, "Don't ask."

THE MIDSUMMER PARADE

It was a beautiful summer day. The breeze was soft, the sun was warm and the birds were singing happily. Elsa and Anna were picking wild flowers in a field not far from town.

"I can't believe it'll be midsummer soon," Anna said, looking around at the lush green meadow.

Elsa grinned. "I love midsummer," she said. "Remember when we were kids and I used to lead–"

"The midsummer parade!" Anna interrupted, finishing her sister's sentence. The midsummer parade was one of her happiest childhood memories.

"I loved that parade," Anna told her sister. "You always looked so fancy, riding at the head of it."

"On that fat little pony," Elsa said, with a chuckle. "Mister Waffles."

This year's parade was shaping up beautifully and Elsa decided that Anna should lead the parade. It was going to be exactly like when Anna and Elsa were kids! Well ... almost exactly.

"I don't think you can ride Mister Waffles in the parade," Elsa told Anna. "You're bigger than he is now. Besides, I'm pretty sure he's retired."

"Then I'll have to find a new horse!" Anna said. "The best horse in all of Arendelle."

Anna and Olaf headed to the stable to find the right horse. "What about that one?" Anna asked the head groom, pointing at an elegant mare.

"She's so pretty!" Olaf sighed admiringly.

"This is Lady Crystalbrook Shinytoes the Fourth," the head groom said.

Lady Crystalbrook Shinytoes the Fourth stepped towards Anna… and tripped over her own feet. She fell right into the pond!

"Oh, dear," Anna said.

Hours later, Anna was at her wit's end. They had met every horse, but they hadn't found the right one. "I don't know what to do," she said miserably. "Maybe we should just cancel the parade."

"Cancel the parade?"

Anna and Olaf looked up to see Kristoff.

"Why would you do that?" he asked.

"I can't find the right horse to lead the parade," Anna said.

"Hmmm," Kristoff said. "I think I know just the fellow for the job."

"You do?" Olaf said. "Who's the horse?"

"Well..." Kristoff said, "he isn't exactly a horse."

"Sven," Kristoff said, slinging his arm around the reindeer's shoulders, "how would you like to lead the parade?"

"Gee whiz," Kristoff said in Sven's voice, speaking for his friend, "I'd be delighted!" And Sven did look delighted.

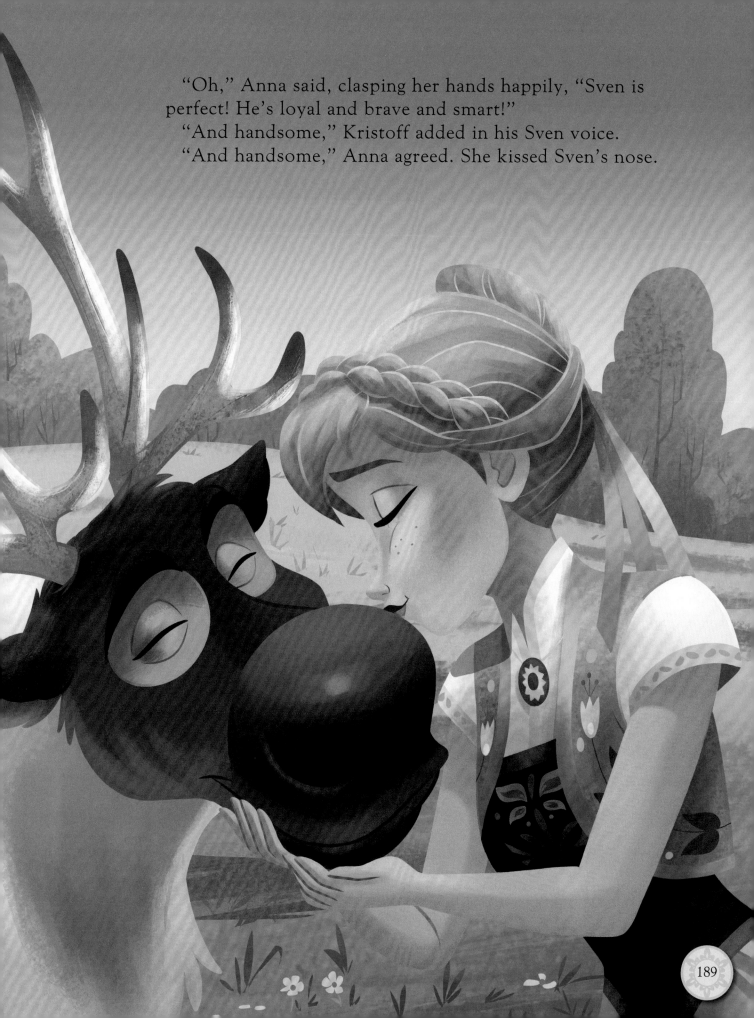

"Oh," Anna said, clasping her hands happily, "Sven is perfect! He's loyal and brave and smart!"

"And handsome," Kristoff added in his Sven voice.

"And handsome," Anna agreed. She kissed Sven's nose.

Anna introduced Sven to the royal stables' grooms. "He's going to be leading the parade with me," she explained, "so he needs to look extra fancy."

"It's an honour," the head groom said, bowing low. "Please come with us, sir."

The grooms set to work on Sven. They oiled his hooves. They polished his antlers. And they brushed and brushed and brushed his fur.

When the royal grooms were done with Sven, he positively shone!

"Sven," Anna said, "you look Svendid!" She elbowed Elsa.
"Get it? Svendid?"

"I get it," Elsa said with a smile. "You really do look magnificent, Sven." Then, she frowned. "But I think there's something missing."

Elsa hung a huge flower wreath around Sven's neck.

"There," she said. "Now you're perfect."

Anna looked at the checklist. "Band, flowers, Sven... I think everything's ready," she said.

Olaf jumped up and down in excitement. "It's parade time!" he cried.

The birds sang, the band played and the people of
Arendelle cheered as the parade wound its way through
town. Anna was so happy she couldn't stop smiling.
The midsummer parade was perfect.

Later, Anna and Elsa celebrated the successful parade. "We did it, Anna!" Elsa said. "The parade was just like when we were kids!" "No," Anna said, grinning at her sister. "It was even better."